A GOPHER
IN THE GARDEN

and Other Animal Poems

A GOPHER
IN THE GARDEN

AND OTHER ANIMAL POEMS

By JACK PRELUTSKY

Pictures by ROBERT LEYDENFROST

The Macmillan Company, New York / Collier-Macmillan Limited, London

The Macmillan Company, New York
Collier-Macmillan Canada, Ltd.,
Toronto, Ontario
Library of Congress catalog
card number : AC 67-10272
Printed in the
United States of America
First Printing

to **Mike Thaler**
for genesis

to the memory
of Ray Calt

Long Gone

Don't waste your time in looking for
the long-extinct tyrannosaur,
because this ancient dinosaur
just can't be found here anymore.

This also goes for stegosaurus,
allosaurus, brontosaurus
and any other saur or saurus.
They all lived here long before us.

The Crocodile

Beware the crafty crocodile
who beckons you with clever smile
to join him in the river Nile
and swim with him a little while.

His smile is not a friendly smile,
it springs from his dishonest guile
and treacherous reptilian style.
Beware the crafty crocodile.

A Gopher in the Garden

There's a gopher in the garden, and he's eating all the onions,
and he's eating all the broccoli and all the beets and beans,
and he's eating all the carrots, all the corn and cauliflower,
all the parsley, peas and pumpkins, all the radishes and greens.

At breakfast, lunch or dinnertime the gopher is no loafer
and he quickly will devour everything before his eyes.
He does not even hesitate to eat a cabbage twice his weight,
or a watermelon five or six or seven times his size.

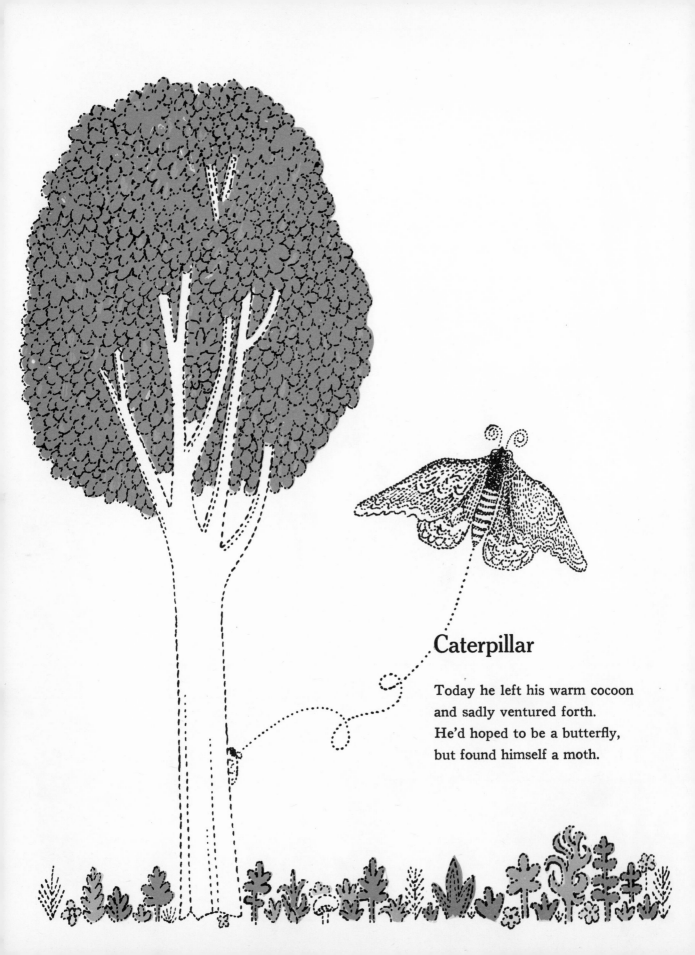

Caterpillar

Today he left his warm cocoon
and sadly ventured forth.
He'd hoped to be a butterfly,
but found himself a moth.

The Shrew

The pygmy shrew is very small,
he almost isn't there at all.
He measures a trifle over an inch
(hardly enough for a healthy pinch).

Scramble

If the zebra were given the spots of the leopard
and the leopard the stripes of the zebra,
then the leopard would have to be renamed the zeopard,
and the zebra retitled the lebra.

And wouldn't we laugh if the gentle giraffe
swapped his neck for the hump on the camel?
For the camel would henceforth be called the camaffe,
the giraffe designated giramel.

It would be very funny, if the ears of the bunny
were exchanged for the horns of the sheep.
For the sheep would then surely be known as the shunny,
and the bunny quite simply the beep.

The Snake

Don't ever make
the bad mistake
of stepping on
the sleeping snake

because
his jaws

might be awake.

Do Not Confuse
the Brindled Gnu

Do not confuse the brindled gnu
with elephant or kangaroo
or lilliputian pygmy shrew
or somewhat larger kinkajou.

And certainly not with mouse or moose
or grebe or grouse or gull or goose
or two-horned black rhinoceros
or hornless hippopotamus,

Or wolf or wolverine or whale
or jumping hare or cottontail
or scented skunk or slowest snail
or chattering crow or quiet quail.

Gibbon, ape or chimpanzee—
the gnu is nothing like these three
and also nothing like the bat
or cat or rat or things like that.

And nothing like the octopus
or little duck-billed platypus
or pointy, prickly porcupine
or jellyfish without a spine,

Or lion, leopard, lynx or loon
or black bear, brown bear, big baboon
or fat and furry ringtailed coon
or coyote baying at the moon.

Or sleepless owl, weary sloth
or butterfly or dreary moth
or any size and shape of monkey,
horse or zebra, mule or donkey.

And for the elk or caribou
you never should mistake the gnu,
and not for egret, erne or eagle,
pointer, setter, boxer, beagle,

Pig or panda, goat or gander,
serpent, seal or salamander,
ground hog, gopher or gorilla,
chicken, chipmunk or chinchilla.

Tortoise, tiger, tapir, teal
or great horned toad or slithering eel,
pigeon, partridge, cow or camel
or <u>any</u> sort of bird or mammal.

The gnu feels very much abused
when for the kudu he's confused,
so if confuse him you must do,
confuse him for . . . another gnu.

The Chipmunk

Chitter-chatter, chitter-chatter
is the chipmunk's steady patter,
even when he's eating acorns
(which he hopes will make him fatter).

The Rabbit

Hip-hop hoppity, hip-hop hoppity,
the rabbit leaps, the rabbit bounds.
His ears are long and soft and floppity,
they let him hear the slightest sounds.

The Giggling Gaggling
Gaggle of Geese

The giggling gaggling gaggle of geese,
they keep all the cows and the chickens awake,
they giggle all night giving nobody peace.
The giggling gaggling gaggle of geese.

The giggling gaggling gaggle of geese,
they chased all the ducks and the swans from the lake.
Oh when will the pranks and the noise ever cease
of the giggling gaggling gaggle of geese!

The giggling gaggling gaggle of geese,
it seems there's no end to the mischief they make,
now they have stolen the sheep's woolen fleece.
The giggling gaggling gaggle of geese,

The giggling gaggling gaggle of geese,
they ate all the cake that the farmer's wife baked.
The mischievous geese are now smug and obese.
The giggling gaggling gaggle of geese.

The giggling gaggling gaggle of geese,
eating that cake was a dreadful mistake.
For when holiday comes they will make a fine feast.
The giggling gaggling gaggle of geese.

The Ostrich

The ostrich believes she is hidden from view
with her foolish head stuck in the ground.
For she thinks you can't see her when she can't see you,
so the ostrich is easily found.

The Owl

The owl is wary, the owl is wise.
He knows all the names of the stars in the skies.
He hoots and he toots and he lives by his wits,
but mostly he sits . . . (and he sits . . . and he sits).

Don't Ever Seize
a Weasel by the Tail

You should never squeeze a weasel
for you might displease the weasel,
and don't ever seize a weasel by the tail.

Let his tail blow in the breeze;
if you pull it, he will sneeze,
for the weasel's constitution tends to be a little frail.

Yes the weasel wheezes easily;
the weasel freezes easily;
the weasel's tan complexion rather suddenly turns pale.

So don't displease or tease a weasel,
squeeze or freeze or wheeze a weasel
and don't ever seize a weasel by the tail.

The Giraffe

The giraffe's long neck provides him
with a most amazing reach.
But though his throat's so lengthy
he's incapable of speech.

The Multilingual
Mynah Bird

Birds are known to cheep and chirp
and sing and warble, peep and purp,
and some can only squeak and squawk,
but the mynah bird is able to talk.

The mynah bird, the mynah bird,
a major, not a minor bird;
you'll never find a finer bird
than the multilingual mynah bird.

He can talk to you in Japanese,
Italian, French and Portuguese;
and even Russian and Chinese
the mynah bird will learn with ease.

The multilingual mynah bird
can say most any word he's heard,
and sometimes he invents a few
(a very difficult thing to do).

So if you want to buy a bird,
why don't you try the mynah bird?
You'll never find a finer bird
than the multilingual mynah bird.

The Bengal Tiger

The Bengal tiger likes to eat
enormous quantities of meat.

Now people have been heard to say
that tigers hypnotize their prey.

So please do not take foolish chances;
avoid the Bengal tiger's glances.

The Egg

If you listen very carefully, you'll hear the chicken hatching.
At first there scarcely was a sound, but now a steady scratching;
and now the egg begins to crack, the scratching starts to quicken,
as anxiously we all await the exit of the chicken.

And now a head emerges from the darkness of the egg,
and now a bit of fluff appears, and now a tiny leg,
and now the chicken's out at last, he's shaking himself loose.
But, wait a minute, that's no chicken . . . goodness, it's a goose.

The Yak

Yickity-yackity, yickity-yak,
the yak has a scriffily, scraffily back;
some yaks are brown yaks and some yaks are black,
yickity-yackity, yickity-yak.

Sniggildy-snaggildy, sniggildy-snag,
the yak is all covered with shiggildy-shag;
he walks with a ziggildy-zaggildy-zag,
sniggildy-snaggildy, sniggildy-snag.

Yickity-yackity, yickity-yak,
the yak has a scriffily, scraffily back;
some yaks are brown yaks and some yaks are black,
yickity-yackity, yickity-yak.

The Wallaby

Oh come and see the wallaby,
the willy wally wallaby,
who bounds about so gracefully
with limitless agility.

The wallaby, the wallaby
defies the laws of gravity
and leaps as high as we can see;
the willy wally wallaby.

Oh come and see the wallaby
who runs and jumps unceasingly,
all filled with merriment and glee;
the willy wally wallaby.

The Three-Toed Sloth

The three-toed sloth is in a deep
and curious and wakeless sleep.
The boughs and branches bend and break,
but seldom does the sloth awake.
The noisy jungle far below
is not for three-toed sloths to know.